Grandmas and
Grandchildren are
Blessings to be Treasured!

♡ Laurie Anne Miller

Grandma Book:

Grandma's Love Is Like No Other

By Laurie Anne Miller

Illustrated by Laurie Anne Miller and Paeton Bavier-Miller

CLAY BRIDGES
PRESS

Grandma Book:

Grandma's Love Is Like No Other

Laurie Anne Miller

DESIGNWISE
GRAPHICS

Grandma Book: Grandma's Love Is Like No Other
First Edition
Copyright © 2021 by Laurie Anne Miller
Illustrations by Laurie Anne Miller and Paeton Bavier-Miller.
Published by Clay Bridges in Houston, TX
www.ClayBridgesPress.com

ISBN: 978-1-953300-90-4 (paperback)
ISBN: 978-1-953300-91-1 (hardback)
eISBN: 978-1-953300-93-5

For Paeton,
the one I hold
so very close
to me!

A special thanks to Alyssa Seppanen, Ramona Scarlett, and Deb Frank for your support in the creation of this book. You always believe I can do what I imagine!

LAURIE ANNE MILLER

Laurie is a grandmother, mother, wife, self-employed graphic designer, writer, photographer, and entrepreneur with two wonderful children and a precious granddaughter. She has always loved making reading a fun and memorable experience! Heartwarming and interactive, you and your grandchild will want to share this keepsake children's book time and again. Laurie, born and raised in Minnesota, lives in the Twin Cities. She has worked in various positions in Graphic Design throughout her career and is currently working on projects through her company, DesignWise Graphics, LLC. She has a degree in Communications/Advertising, along with a minor in Commercial Economics, from South Dakota State University.

Interactive Books With A Loving Message

Designed for fun and interaction! Both you and your grandchild will enjoy your journey through the pages with Honeybee, a sweet, inquisitive character that will surely add joy to your adventure. Along with a loving message, there are many learning opportunities and great ideas for fun activities to share with your precious grandchild.

Especially For

_____

My little Cuddle Bug,
You are Grandma's greatest JOY!

Hi! I'm
Honeybee
Don't mind me,
I'm just passing
through!

A Favorite Memory
of You and Me...

_____

_____

_____

_____

_____

Love & Hugs, _____

Date: _____

You are a child of God. You are wonderfully made, dearly loved, and precious in His sight. ~ Psalm 139

Sweet and PERFECT in every way,
Heaven sent you I know.
The very moment I met you,
My HEART melted and began to grow!

My, my! Grandmas
have really BIG HEARTS!
Where is your HEART?
Can YOU FIND all the
HEARTS on this page?

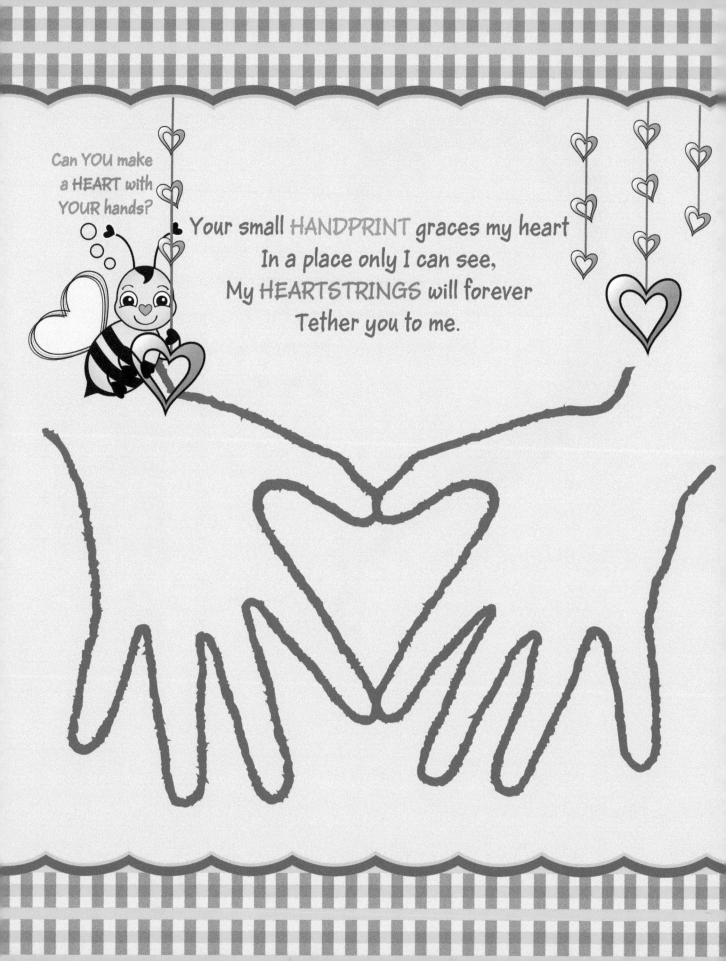

Can YOU make a HEART with YOUR hands?

Your small HANDPRINT graces my heart
In a place only I can see,
My HEARTSTRINGS will forever
Tether you to me.

The rarest of GEMS,
You are more precious to me
Than all the TREASURES of the world
Could possibly ever be.

Wow! YOU are WORTH LOTS!
What TREASURES do YOU find here?

You are my **SUNSHINE**, my little angel,
My cuddle-bug, and my sweet pea.
I love you to the **SUN** and back,
Much farther than you can see!

Hmmm, that is **REALLY FAR!** How far can **YOU SEE** with **YOUR** eyes?

While I tenderly hold you,
You are sure to find
A special place in GRANDMA'S ARMS,
Always so very LOVING and KIND.

Awwwe,
Can YOU give YOUR
GRANDMA a BIG HUG too?

Let's **SING** your favorite songs
And recite age-old **NURSERY RHYMES.**

Can YOU say these NURSERY RHYMES?
How many STARS do YOU see on this page?

Share lots of BOOKS and GRANDMA HUGS.
And tell the STORIES of past times.

What is a favorite STORY Grandma tells about YOU?

Nursery Rhymes

1 2 3 4 5 6 7 8 9 10

You have ten little **FINGERS** and ten little **TOES**,
So let's **COUNT** each and every one.

Can **YOU** make **PRINTS** with **YOUR** **HANDS** and **FEET?** What is the **HIGHEST** **NUMBER YOU** can **COUNT** to?

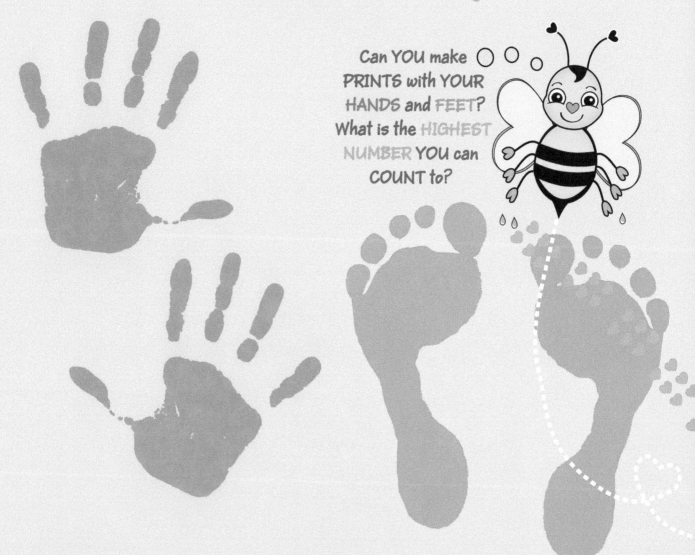

Now, let's start **OVER** and count them again,
Because counting is so much **FUN!**

Lay your small **HAND** on this page,
Let's **TRACE** around each and every finger.

Age: _____

Date: _____

Hmmm,
I bet MINE are
the SMALLEST!
Now YOU have a
drawing of YOUR
HANDS to keep
FOREVER!

I will trace **MY HAND** over yours,
Can you tell me whose hand is **BIGGER**?

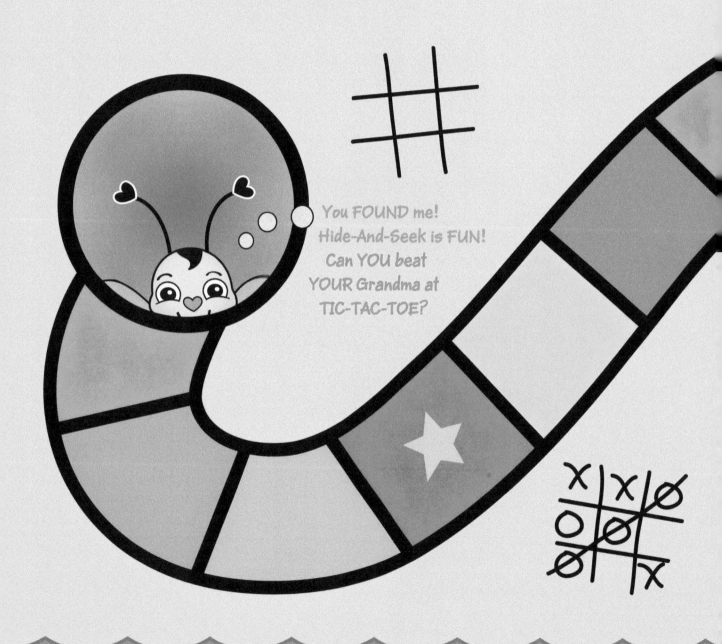

Oh, the **GAMES** we like to play...
Especially **CANDY LAND**, Tic-Tac-Toe, and Hide-And-Seek.

You FOUND me!
Hide-And-Seek is FUN!
Can YOU beat
YOUR Grandma at
TIC-TAC-TOE?

"Simon Says" you love Old Maid and Go Fish,
And when we play MEMORY, I sometimes let you PEEK!

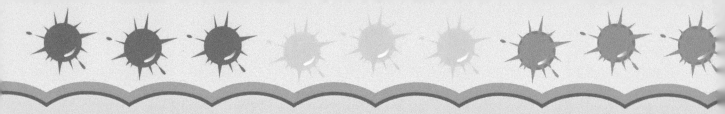

Let's create beautiful MASTERPIECES
With our crayons and our paints.
In a HOT PINK DRESS and a SMILE,
I will certainly have NO complaints!

What is YOUR
favorite COLOR?

_____

What is YOUR
Grandma's favorite
COLOR?

_____

Grandma

Together we can EXPLORE the world
And share GREAT ADVENTURES on Grandma days.
With all the things I want to teach you,
LEARNING will be FUN in so many ways!

Wow! YOU look GINORMOUS!
Have YOU seen a CATERPILLAR?
Do YOU know how a caterpillar
becomes a BUTTERFLY?

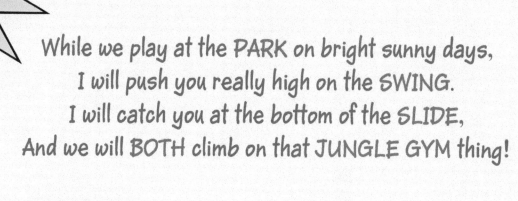

While we play at the PARK on bright sunny days,
I will push you really high on the SWING.
I will catch you at the bottom of the SLIDE,
And we will BOTH climb on that JUNGLE GYM thing!

WHEEEE!
This is FUN!
Do you like the
SLIDE, SWINGS,
or JUNGLE GYM
the BEST? WHY?

Ouch!!!
The SLIDE
is BRUTAL!

A trip to the ZOO is oodles of fun
With so many animals to see.
The MONKEYS like to chatter and swing,
And the LIONS and TIGERS will flee.

Which ZOO
ANIMAL do
YOU like best?

But that is all a part of life,
And when you feel SAD and BROKEN
GRANDMA will always be right here
With lots of HUGS and CARING WORDS spoken.

Oh, Dear!
I don't think a
bandage will fix THIS!
When have YOU
been SO SAD?

Let's catch LIGHTNING BUGS as they come out to play
And trace their PATHS as they flitter and fly.

Pfshew!
Can YOU TRACE
the LIGHTNING
BUGS' PATHS with
YOUR finger?

Then, RELEASE them from our big glass jar
And watch in amazement as they LIGHT UP the evening sky!

AWESOME!
How many
LIGHTNING BUGS
do YOU see dancing
in the sky?

Look at
all the STARS!
Can YOU find the
LITTLE DIPPER,
the BIG DIPPER,
and the NORTH
STAR too?

While this great UNIVERSE
May seem awfully large,
No matter where you may go
I will NEVER, EVER be far.

GRANDMAS
are THE BEST!
Can YOU find the
PINK POODLE
that is
DIFFERENT
from the rest?

At bedtime, we will READ your favorite book
Over and over and then,
When you beg, "Please, just ONE more time?",
Of course, we will read it AGAIN!

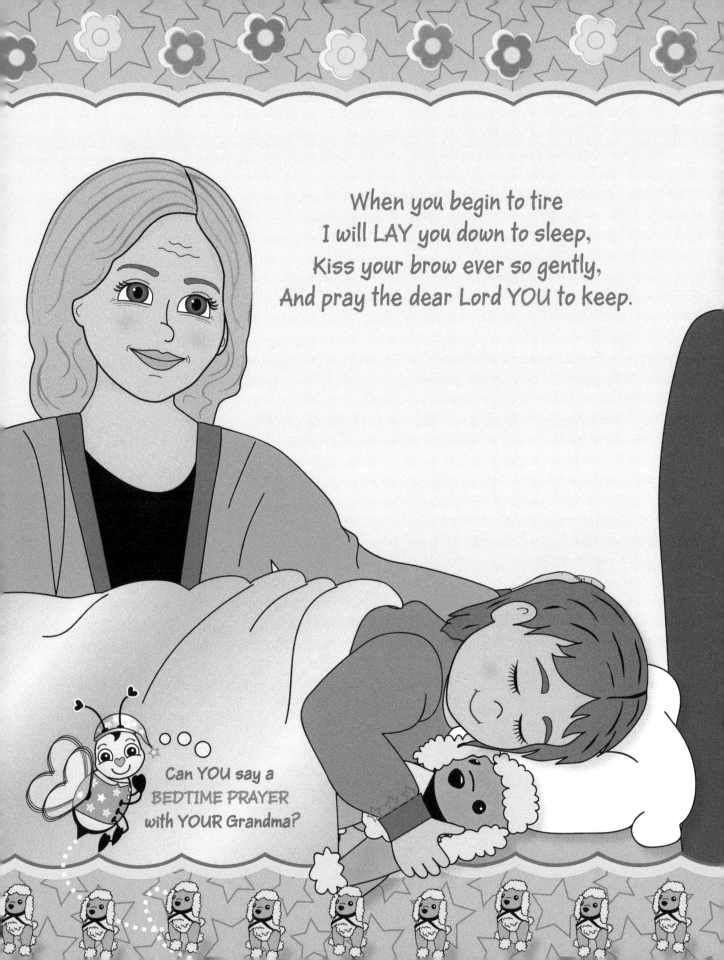

When you begin to tire
I will LAY you down to sleep,
Kiss your brow ever so gently,
And pray the dear Lord YOU to keep.

Can YOU say a
BEDTIME PRAYER
with YOUR Grandma?

I will watch over you as you lie in peaceful slumber,
Your **HAND** tucked in mine as softly as ever.
Though your small hand I will hold for only a short while,
Your **HEART** I will hold **ALWAYS** and **FOREVER**.

'Cause you know,
GRANDMA'S LOVE is LIKE NO OTHER
And never will you be
More LOVED than when I hold you
So very close to me.

SMILE!

Grandma and Me

Photo of My
Grandma and Me

A Love Like No Other!

CPSIA information can be obtained
at www.ICGtesting.com
Printed in the USA
BVHW021733090222
628404BV00002BA/29